Sierra the Search Dog
Finds Fred

by Robert D. Calkins
Illustrated by Taillefer Long

SIERRA THE SEARCH DOG FINDS FRED
by Robert D. Calkins

CALLOUT PRESS
Olalla, Washington
SierraSearchDog.com
RobertDCalkins.com

Illustrations and Design by Taillefer Long
info@IlluminatedStories.com

ISBN: 978-0-9971911-4-1
Library of Congress Control Number: 2016938775

Dedicated to K9 Magnum, Sierra's younger
brother, who for ten years carried on her legacy
of service to the people of Washington state.

Sierra the Search Dog Finds Fred

by Robert D. Calkins

Illustrated by Taillefer Long

"Where's Fred?" wondered Ted.
He went to the store to buy some bread.
But he didn't come back. Oh, where is Fred?

Ted thought for a second, and used his head.
He looked all over for signs of Fred.

Is he under the bed?

Is he in the shed?

Nope!

Is he on the sled?

Is he in the house
that's brick, and red?

Ted looked really hard but
he couldn't find Fred.

Ted was upset, his mind in a fog.
But he thought of Sierra, his cousin's search dog.

He called Cousin Bryce to ask for his aid.
They had to find Fred, wherever he'd strayed.

Bryce said, "Of course, Sierra will find him.
She'll follow his scent, it stays right behind him."

In no time at all, Sierra was there,
A Golden Retriever with lovely blonde hair.

She was wearing her harness all shiny and red.
She'd found other people. Today she'd find Fred.

But she needed something of Fred's to smell,
'Cuz that's how a search dog follows so well.

Ted went to the closet and found an old shoe.
It was Fred's favorite sneaker—eewww . . . P-U!

Bryce and Ted held their noses, it really smelled bad.
But Sierra, she loved it . . . she licked it a tad.

She snorted and sniffed and got a good snootful.
Fred's odor was there. It was really a bootful.

FUN FACTS

In the woods, some search dogs work without a leash, and might be far away from their handler. When the dog finds the missing person, it returns to the handler and gives a special signal that says "found 'em!" Some dogs sit. Some dogs jump up on the handler. Others bark, or even tug at a toy on the handler's belt.

Sierra then turned, and bolted forth,
To search for Fred. She first went north.
Her nose said, "Not here," as she went down the street.
No sign of Fred or his stinky feet.

So Sierra turned right and sniffed some more.
First she sniffed at the candy store.
She went upstairs and sniffed the floor.
She went to the beach and sniffed the shore.
And then she sniffed the old church door.

Her tail shot up, her nose went down.
It was Fred she smelled, he'd gone to town.

FUN FACTS

Just as humans identify individual sounds, dogs recognize specific smells. In a pizza parlor, for example, not only would a dog smell the pizzas, she would also be able to pick out the smell of each topping.

Bryce asked the preacher and yes, it was true.
Fred had been there, all dressed in blue.
But he didn't see which way Fred had gone.
Was it down the street or across the lawn?

FUN FACTS

Search dogs need to be able to stop searching and wait patiently while their handler talks to people who might have seen the missing person. Once everyone is done talking, a good search dog will go back to sniffing, right where they left off.

Well Sierra could tell, it was down the street.
And off she went, not missing a beat.

Around the corner and down the block,
Right on past the old town clock.

Up Main Street, she turned on Third,
Right on past the chirping bird.

Down the hill and over the bridge,
Sierra stopped, and went back a smidge.

Tic Toc Tic Toc

MAIN

Sniff Sniff

S.A.R.

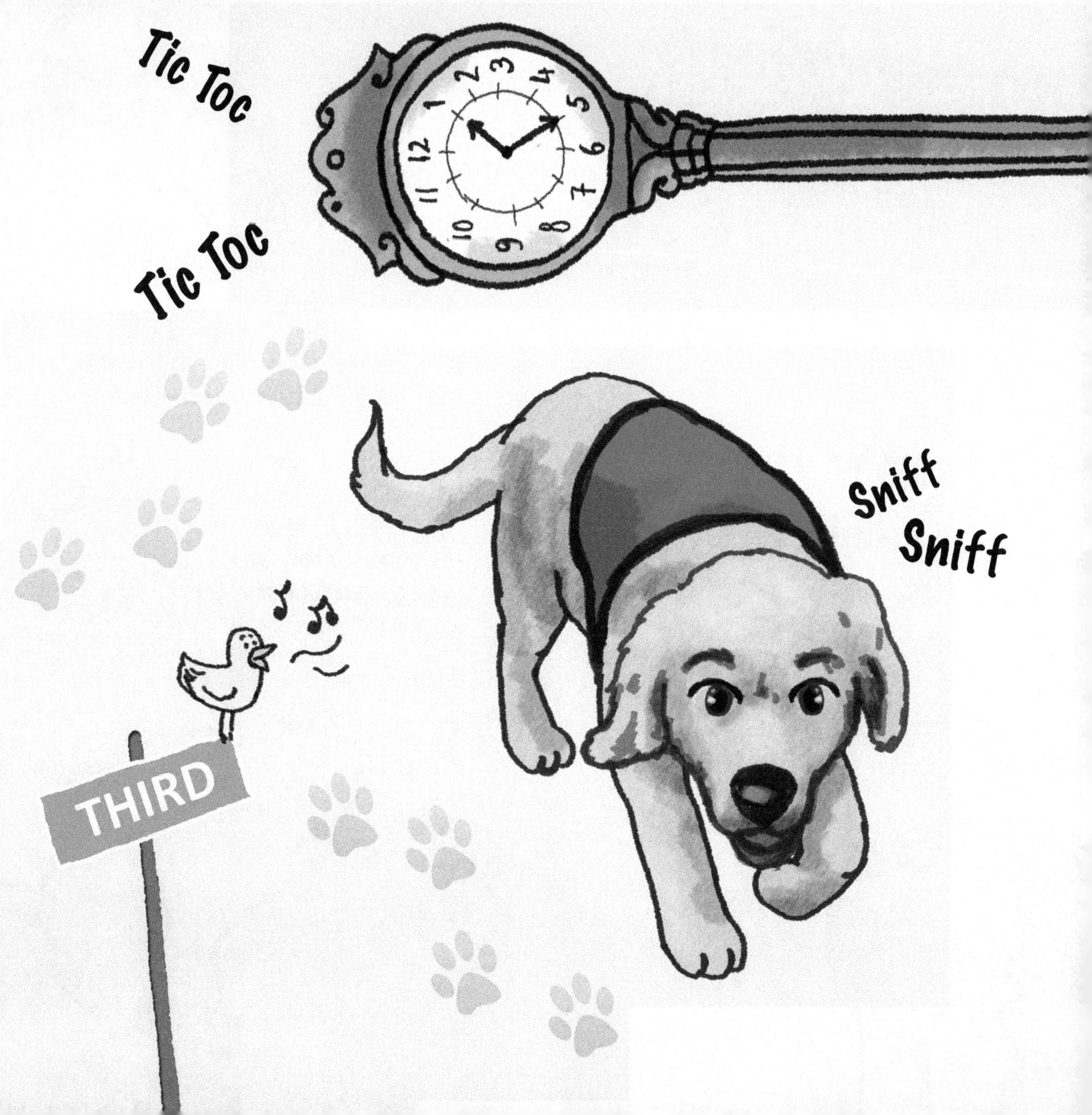
Tic Toc
Tic Toc
Sniff
Sniff
THIRD

FUN FACTS

Sniff

She put up her nose, and sniffed the air.
The walking path—Fred had been there.

She only needed to figure which way.
Her nose would tell her, it would not stray.

She first sniffed left and then sniffed right.
Then off she went, her leash pulled tight.

Sniff
Sniff

Sniff
Sniff

She trotted along the bank of the river.
Her nose was down, her tail a-quiver.

And then she found them. Two real clues.
There by the path . . . both of Fred's shoes.

But right beside were shoes galore,
So many it looked like a big shoe store.

In the nearby field, people were dancing.
Barefoot and twirling, there was even some prancing.

The search team walked over and joined the crowd.
Ted called for Fred but the music was loud.

No one could hear Ted calling Fred's name.
To Sierra though, this was her game.

She went through the crowd, and used her nose.
She sniffed each dancer, especially their toes.

Pretty soon the answer was clear.
Sierra had done it. Fred was right here.

Ted told Fred, "I've been worried sick.
Were you trying to play some awful trick?"

"No trick," said Fred. "If I'd known you were worried,
I'd have skipped the dancing and home would have hurried.

"But the music was awesome, the people were fun.
I couldn't help dancing barefoot in the sun."

FUN FACTS

One of the most important things when training a search dog is to get them used to distractions like loud noises. A search dog needs to be able to focus on its job around other animals, people, cars, or even helicopters.

The music WAS awesome, the rhythm was neat.
Sierra was wagging her tail to the beat.

They danced and they sang, every Mister and Missus.
And Sierra gave everyone wet puppy kisses.

About the Author

Robert "Bob" Calkins has been a search and rescue dog handler in Kitsap County, Washington, for more than a dozen years. Bob currently searches with K9 Ruger, a four-year old Golden Retriever who passed his SAR test in the spring of 2015. He and his dogs have responded to everything from routine missing person cases, to homicides, to the horrific landslide that in 2014 swept over homes in the tiny community of Oso, Washington.

Bob is the author of the **SIERRA THE SEARCH DOG** series of books for children and adults.

About the Real Sierra

Sierra was Bob's first search dog, a Golden Retriever with the well-known "Golden smile" and a natural ability to find people who'd gotten lost. She liked nothing better than running through the woods hoping to pick up the scent of a missing person. Her paycheck was a simple tennis ball, and a scratch on the head. She worked with Bob for five years, responding to many missing person searches in and around western Washington.

About the Illustrator

Taillefer Long is an illustrator and designer based in Charleston, SC. He loves visual storytelling, the creative process, and seeing ideas come to life. Taillefer has collaborated with many authors, illustrating and designing books for over a decade. His childhood Basset Hound, Aesop, was an expert cuddler and drooler but could have used a little obedience training from Bob!

Taillefer's work can be found at IlluminatedStories.com and DancingInkArt.com.

CPSIA information can be obtained
at www.ICGtesting.com
Printed in the USA
LVHW06s2030230318
571043LV00004B/59/P

9 780997 191141